Santa
and his Sleigh

It was a snowy Christmas Eve at the North Pole, and Santa was so excited!

"Just a few more hours," he beamed, "and then we'll be on our way. I can't wait to drive my sleigh tonight!" Santa rubbed his hands in delight.

Now of course, Santa's favorite part of his job is giving gifts. But driving a flying sleigh is very exciting, and Santa gets pretty jolly whenever he thinks about it! So do the reindeer. They love to fly!

Everything was nearly ready. The reindeer were prancing around, the snow was drifting down, and the elves were adding ribbons and bows to the last few gifts.

How does Santa's sleigh fly? Is it the elves who keep it polished and bright? Is it the reindeer? Without magic, Santa's sleigh could never fly around the world, not even with the fastest reindeer in all of the North Pole.

It's partly Santa, because he's a pretty special guy, and it's partly the reindeer, because magic helps them fly, but it's also a third thing. Can you guess what it might be?

Emily the reindeer was very young, and this was her first Christmas Eve helping out. She was very curious about Santa's magical sleigh and what made it fly.

Just before twilight, Santa's elves posted a sign on an old tree. They had been checking inventory and made an interesting discovery. "Congratulations everyone! This will be the biggest Christmas Eve delivery in the history of the North Pole!"

Everyone gathered around to read the exciting news. This would be a Christmas to remember for years to come! They were so proud to be part of the biggest Christmas Eve delivery ever!

Biggest Ever!

"Why, this is the longest list I've ever seen!" exclaimed Santa.
"The world just gets bigger and bigger! There are so many good
children waiting for us!"

Emily was worried. Even with all the magic in the North Pole, even with Santa and the elves and the reindeer, how would the heavy sleigh fly all the way around the world?

None of the other creatures seemed to be concerned. They were playing in the snow and celebrating. Emily watched from behind a tree and wondered about the sleigh. Would it make it all the way? Would all the toys get delivered on time?

Santa always knows what his reindeer are thinking. "Don't fret, little Emily!" he told her, "There's more magic than ever this year. We'll get all the gifts delivered, don't you fear!"

"Now the stockings are hung, and the sleigh is all ready. We'll be just fine, if we take it slow and steady!"

But where was the magic? Emily hunted all around. Was it in the holly bushes, or on the snowy ground?

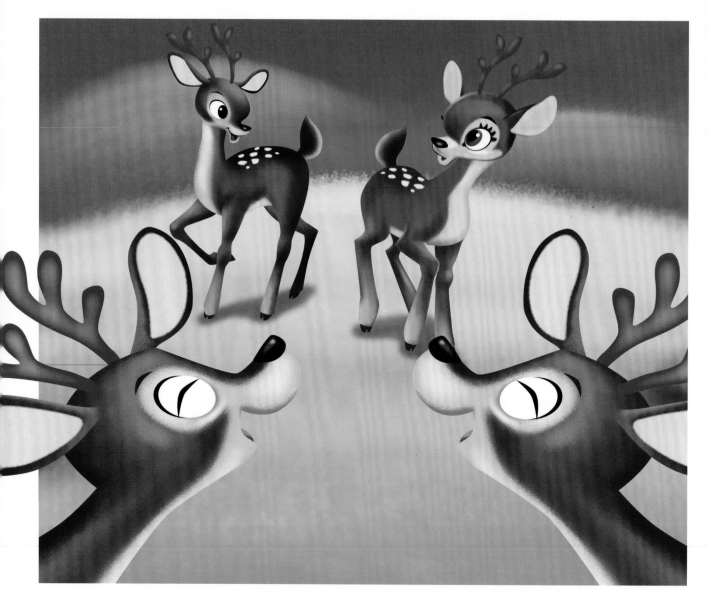

"How do we know we've got enough magic to go all around the whole world?" Emily asked the other reindeer.

"What a silly question!" they all laughed.

The news spread quickly, "Did you hear? Emily the reindeer doesn't think Santa's sleigh can go all the way around the world!"

Emily was so embarrassed! Everyone was laughing at her.

Santa called all the helpers together. "It's nearly time to get on our way! I know one little reindeer is worried about my sleigh. But there's no need to worry, there's no need to fuss, the children are waiting, so get there we must!"

18

"I'll tell you a secret about my sleigh. The magic doesn't come from elves making toys. It isn't from giftwrap, or stocking stuffers or noisemakers! It isn't from candy canes, or even Christmas songs. It's something much bigger, and it's very, very strong!"

Emily thought hard. If it isn't from elves, or decorating trees, if it isn't sweets or bunnies, then what else could it be? Is it just Santa?

"No, it's not just me! It's something very special, and it's growing fast."

Finally Emily understood at last! "I know, Santa! I know what drives your sleigh! I know what makes it fly the whole, long way!"

Every time a child does something kind, tries to be helpful,
and careful, and brave, it makes the sleigh fly. It goes magically fast.

Sometimes, it's hard to be good, but everyone tries. We know this is true, because the sleigh always flies!

As Santa and his magic sleigh flew off into the sky, Emily smiled, because she knew how and why.